WHERE'S THE
UNICORN?
ACTIVITY BOOK

This book belongs to: billie.

WHERE'S THE UNICORN? ACTIVITY BOOK

ILLUSTRATED BY JORGE SANTILLAN AND PAUL MORAN

WRITTEN BY IMOGEN CURRELL-WILLIAMS

DESIGNED BY ZOE BRADLEY

Buster Books

Introduction

The seven unicorns of Rainbow Valley are ready
for an activity adventure. This book is filled with all sorts
of puzzle challenges, from odd ones out and spot the differences
to search-and-find scenes and cool colouring pages.

Follow the instructions at the top of each page and, when you've
finished, you can find all the answers at the back of the book.

Now, grab a pen and get ready
for some magical unicorn fun.

Adventure Trail

Amethyst is going on an adventure. Follow the hoofprints from the castle to find out which trail she left in the snow.

A. B. C. D.

1.

2.

3.

4.

Woodland Wander

The unicorns have come to play in the woods.
Can you spot the ten differences
between these two scenes?

Ice Rink Puzzle

The unicorns are trying out their ice-skating skills.
Leaf has taken to it like a duck to water, but Ruby isn't so sure.
How many of the tiles below do not appear in this ice-skating scene?

A.

B.

C.

D.

E.

F.

G.

H.

Magical Maze Mayhem

Ruby has been separated from her unicorn friends.
Help her through the maze to get back to Stardust, Snowflake
and Blossom. You can eat apples and cupcakes as you go, but watch
out for poisonous toadstools and unicorn poo that you cannot pass.

START

FINISH

11

Fishing Trip

It's time for a trip to the sea.
Follow the tangled lines to reveal
what each unicorn has caught.

Cupcake Conundrum

Can you find these three groups of cupcakes among the tasty treats below?

Supersonic
Search

The unicorns have travelled
into the future and are exploring
a whole new world.

Stardust has settled straight in and
is enjoying his spacemobile. Ruby
prefers the safety of home and is
trying to make a swift exit.

Can you spot all seven
unicorns in this scene?

Kitchen Chaos

It's time to do some baking but the unicorns have forgotten which recipe to use. Look at the ingredients pictured on the right and work out which recipe card features the correct ingredients.

Recipe 1

Butter
Six eggs
Sugar
Edible ears
Flour
Marshmallows
Icing
Marzipan horn

Recipe 2

Marshmallows
Sugar
Flour
Butter
Icing
Marzipan horn
Six eggs

Recipe 3

Sugar
Seven eggs
Marshmallows
Flour
Butter
Edible ears
Marzipan horn

BUTTER

EGGS

SUGAR

FLOUR

ICING

EDIBLE EARS

MARZIPAN HORN

MARSHMALLOWS

Gallery Search and Find

The seven unicorns of Rainbow Valley are having a day out at a modern art gallery. Can you find them all, and then help them count the things on their checklist too?

Checklist:
Cameras ....
Security guards ....
Blue backpacks ....
Sketchbooks ....

Splish Splash

The unicorns have come for a day out at the water park. Can you spot the 15 differences between these two pictures?

Who Pooped?

One of the unicorns has left a magical poo at the end of their rainbow. Can you follow the rainbow paths to find out who it was?

C.

D.

E.

4.

5.

Sahara Search

The unicorns are out in the desert getting to know this group of camels who are about to set off on a long trek.

Blossom has found her place among the camels, but Luna has decided she would rather relax and has found herself a comfortable ride for the journey.

Can you spot all seven unicorns in this scene?

Beach Trip

Colour in this sunny scene.

Sequence Solver

Look at the sequences of unicorns below.
Can you work out which unicorn
would come next in each row?

A.

B.

C.

Unicorn Jumble

How many unicorns can you count in the jumble below?

Which Unicorn Are You?

Answer the questions in this flowchart to find out which unicorn you would be. Then turn the page to find out more about each type of unicorn.

Start
Where would you rather go on holiday?

A log cabin in peaceful woods, surrounded by wildlife.

When you're out walking in the woods, you are approached by a bear. What do you do?

Try to reassure the bear you won't cause it any harm and walk away calmly.

Immediately plan how you are going to escape and run away.

A sunny beach on a remote island with all your friends.

There is lots to explore on the island. What do you do?

Make a list of all the things you want to see and work out when you can visit them.

You've come on holiday to relax on the beach, not spend all day sightseeing!

You bump into a friend. What do you do?

You politely say hello and then keep walking.

Snowflake

You ask them to join you – you're going on an adventure.

Leaf

Keep going. The weather won't get in the way of your expedition.

The weather takes a turn and it starts to pour with rain. What do you do?

Get your raincoat out of your backpack and head home. You are prepared for all situations.

Ruby

Luckily, you learnt how to ask for your favourite food before you came on holiday, so you can order exactly what you want.

Blossom

You're at a restaurant but the menu is in a different language. What do you do?

You decide to be brave and randomly point at something on the menu.

Stardust

It's time to party! You call all your friends and tell them where to meet you.

Luna

You discover a new beach hidden away in a cove. What do you do?

Finally, some peace and quiet. Time to relax and read your new book.

Amethyst

Your Unicorn Traits

Find out what your answer reveals about you.

Snowflake

You are wise and sensitive, and keep a close-knit group of friends around you. Although you might not have the loudest voice in the room, you're always there for your friends and make time to listen to them and offer advice.

Leaf

You are a fearless explorer and are always going off on adventures in the hope of discovering new things. You love it when your friends come along on your expeditions, but even when they can't join you, you're not afraid to go by yourself.

Ruby

You are an excellent organizer and love nothing more than to plan group activities for all of your friends. You surround yourself with lots of friends and will always welcome new people into your gang and make them feel at home.

Blossom

You are more quiet and sensible than some of your friends, and instead of rushing into decisions you prefer to take your time to think about all the options before making a choice. Your friends know they can trust you to give them honest and thoughtful advice.

Stardust

You love to laugh and joke and don't take life too seriously. You're always thinking of funny jokes to crack that will make everyone laugh. You are surrounded by friends who love your sense of humour and like to have fun with you.

Luna

You have a zest for life and are always busy making new and exciting plans. You love to bring all your friends together to have fun and are always full of bright ideas for new activities you can try out. You are surrounded by friends who love your passion and enthusiasm.

Amethyst

You love nothing more than burying your head in a good book and getting lost in a story. You are very creative and love to learn new skills. You are surrounded by people who you can have interesting conversations with about all the things you have discovered.

Odd Ones Out

Can you find the three unicorns that don't match the others?

Pattern Puzzle

Can you find a way through this grid from start to finish? You can move up, down, left and right but not diagonally. Follow the pictures in the order shown in the panel at the top.

UNICORN POO

UNICORN CUPCAKE

UNICORN HORN

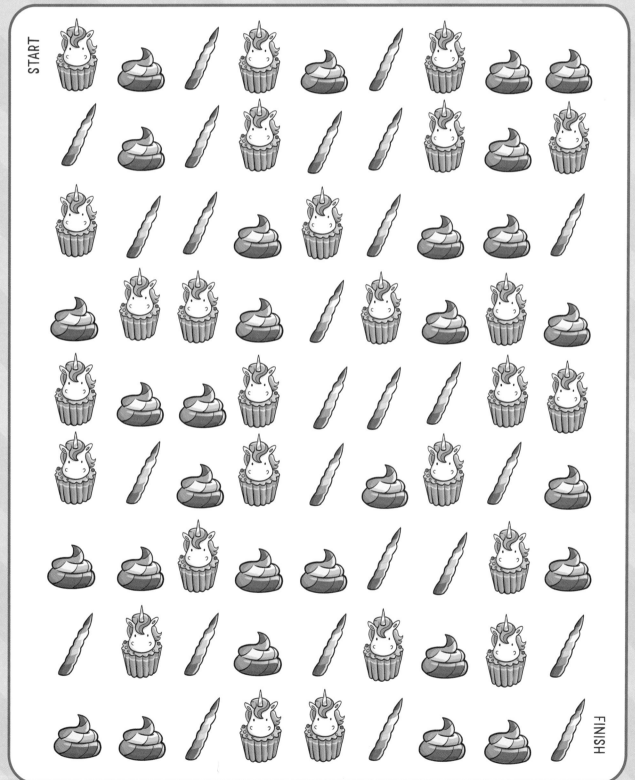

START

FINISH

Pirate Battle

Ahoy there! The unicorns have found themselves in the middle of a pirate battle on the high seas.

Blossom is preparing for a duel while Snowflake considers jumping ship.

Can you spot all seven unicorns in this scene?

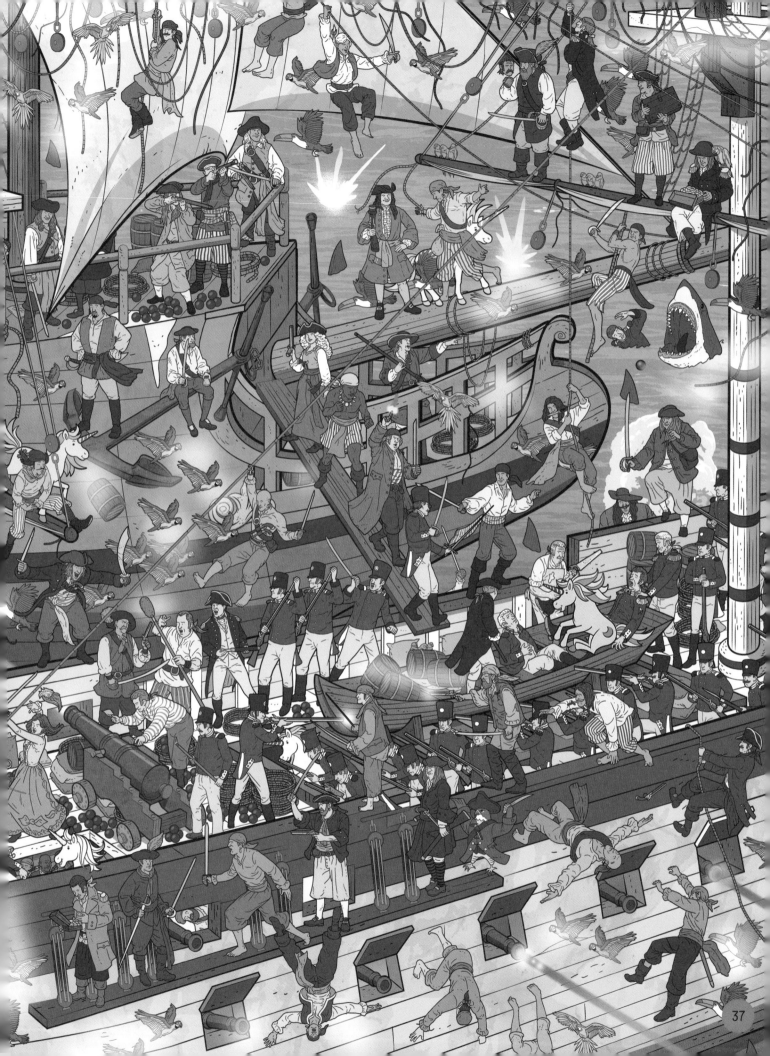

Fairground Fun

Stardust, Leaf, Amethyst and Luna have gone to the fairground. They each want to go to a different attraction. Follow the paths to find out what each unicorn wants to visit.

STARDUST

LUNA

Spot the Silhouettes

The seven unicorns of Rainbow Valley have travelled to a sandy desert, but they have lost their shadows. Can you match them up?

A.

B.

C.

D.

E.

F.

G.

Magical Meadow

Colour in Luna.

Symbol Count

How many of each unicorn symbol can you count below?

Key:

DIAMOND   SNOWFLAKE   FLOWER   STAR   MOON   HEART   CLOVER

43

Mountain Mayhem

Which of the jigsaw pieces below cannot be found in this ski slope scene?

A.

B.

C.

D.

E.

F.

G.

H.

Ancient Egypt

The unicorns of Rainbow Valley have travelled back in time and are exploring the River Nile.

Blossom has taken a shine to the high life, while Stardust is just trying to blend in.

Can you spot all seven unicorns in this scene?

47

Unicorn Search

This group of unicorns has gathered in a woodland clearing to frolic and play. Comet has just joined them all. Can you read the clues below to work out which unicorn she is?

Comet has:

Two legs up

Four stripes on her tail

Eight stripes on her horn

Open eyes

Moon stamp

Coral Reef Counting

The seven unicorns of Rainbow Valley have gone on a diving expedition. Can you find them all and help them count the animals on their checklist?

It's Bingo Time!

It's Snowflake's birthday party. Can you find all the things on the birthday bingo cards? Challenge a friend to see who can find them first.

UNICORN TOY

BALLOON

FIZZY DRINK

PARTY HAT

CHOCOLATE CUPCAKE

PARTY HORN

LEMONADE

BALL

SANDWICHES

VANILLA CUPCAKE

CUP AND SAUCER

PRESENT

JUG OF LEMONADE

GOLDEN CROWN

TEDDY BEAR

UNICORN CAKE

LOLLIPOPS

SWEETS

Pair Them Up

Can you match the ten identical pairs of unicorns?

Under a Rainbow

There are five rainbows that don't match the others. Can you find them?

All the Answers

Adventure Trail p.5

A–4
B–1
C–3
D–2

Woodland Wander p.6-7

Ice Rink Puzzle p.8-9

C.

D.

F.

H.

Magical Maze Mayham p.10-11

Fishing Trip p.12

A–3
B–1
C–2
D–4

Cupcake Conundrum p.13

Supersonic Search p.14-15

Kitchen Chaos p.16

Recipe 1 is correct.

Gallery Search and Find p.18-19

Cameras – 4
Security guards – 5
Blue backpacks – 1
Sketchbooks – 2

Splish Splash p.20-21

Sahara Search p.24-25

Sequence Solver p.28

Who Pooped? p.22-23

A–5
B–4
C–1
D–3
E–2

Unicorn Jumble p.29

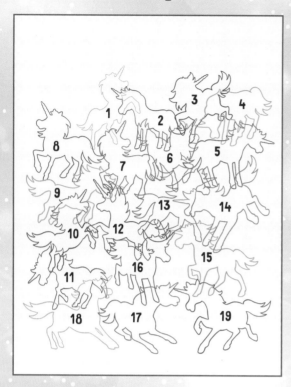

19 unicorns

Odd Ones Out p.34

Pattern Puzzle p.35

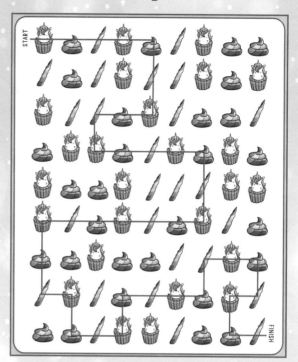

Pirate Party p.36-37

Fairground Fun p.38-39

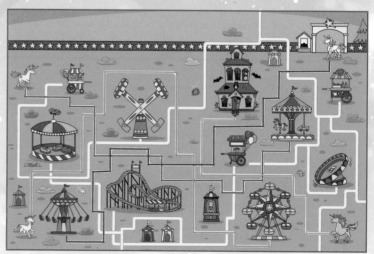

Spot the Silhouettes p.40-41

A–6
B–5
C–7
D–1
E–4
F–2
G–3

Symbol Count p.43

Diamonds – 17
Snowflakes – 11
Flowers – 9
Stars – 15
Moons – 7
Hearts – 12
Clovers – 12

Mountain Mayhem p.44-45

A.
D.
F.
G.

Ancient Egypt p.46-47

Unicorn Search p.48-49

Coral Reef Counting p.50-51

Crabs – 3
Starfish – 5
Turtles – 2
Clownfish – 6

It's Bingo Time! p.52-53

Pair Them Up p.54-55

Under a Rainbow p.56